SRA

Lesson
Assessment
Book 2

Blackline Masters

Level 5

Mc Graw Hill **SRA**

A Division of The **McGraw-Hill** Companies

SRAonline.com

 SRA

Copyright © 2008 by SRA/McGraw-Hill.

Printed in the United States of America.

Send all inquiries to this address:
SRA/McGraw-Hill
4400 Easton Commons
Columbus, OH 43219-6188

ISBN: 978-0-07-613230-0
MHID: 0-07-613230-7

2 3 4 5 6 7 8 9   MAZ 13 12 11 10 09 08 07

Table of Contents

Name _____ Date _____ Score _____

The Universe

Vocabulary

Read each item. Fill in the bubble for the answer you think is correct.

1. The Greek root **scope** means
   - Ⓐ to look.
   - Ⓑ to speak.
   - Ⓒ to listen.
   - Ⓓ to sell.

2. To **detect** means to
   - Ⓐ explode.
   - Ⓑ prove.
   - Ⓒ guess.
   - Ⓓ notice.

3. New stars are the bright lights inside the **bulges** at the top of the nebula. **Bulges** are
   - Ⓐ rounded parts that swell out.
   - Ⓑ measurements used in space.
   - Ⓒ lights seen without telescopes.
   - Ⓓ dark clouds that drift apart.

4. The Milky Way Galaxy is a vast **spiral** of stars. A **spiral** is
   - Ⓐ a globe that rotates.
   - Ⓑ a narrow jet of clouds.
   - Ⓒ a curve that keeps winding.
   - Ⓓ a series of rings made of gases.

5. The universe may keep expanding, or it may eventually **collapse.** To **collapse** means to
   - Ⓐ come back around.
   - Ⓑ fall in on itself.
   - Ⓒ stick together.
   - Ⓓ rebuild itself.

The Universe (continued)

Comprehension

Read the following questions carefully. Then completely fill in the bubble of each correct answer. You may look back at the selection to find the answer to each of the questions.

1. Which of these is classified as a star?

Ⓐ the Sun

Ⓑ the Moon

Ⓒ Earth

Ⓓ the Galaxy

2. Which statement about the Moon is true?

Ⓐ It is sometimes called Alpha Centauri.

Ⓑ It is one of the "inner planets."

Ⓒ It is Earth's nearest neighbor in space.

Ⓓ It is at the center of our galaxy.

The Universe (continued)

3. Jupiter and Saturn are both examples of

Ⓐ young stars.

Ⓑ giant outer planets.

Ⓒ distant galaxies.

Ⓓ new nebula clusters.

4. What causes scientists to believe they may find other solar systems?

Ⓐ the improvement in telescope technology

Ⓑ the age of the inner and outer planets

Ⓒ the number of new planets being found

Ⓓ the gas-and-dust disks forming around young stars

5. A planetary nebula is

Ⓐ a cluster of new stars being born.

Ⓑ a new planet in the making.

Ⓒ a cloud of glowing gases around an aging star.

Ⓓ a dead star that roams throughout the galaxy.

The Universe (continued)

Read the following questions carefully. Use complete sentences to answer the questions.

6. Explain what a light-year is and how it is used.

_____

_____

7. How do planetary nebulas differ from one another?

_____

_____

8. Why does the author use the phrase "our lonely part of space" to describe our position in the Milky Way?

_____

_____

9. At the end of the selection, the author asks a series of questions. What do these questions suggest about humankind's knowledge about space?

_____

_____

10. What is a black hole?

_____

_____

The Universe (continued)

Read the question below. Write complete sentences for your answer. Support your answer with information from the selection.

Linking to the Concepts How is the address at the beginning of the selection helpful as an introduction to the topic of space?

_____

_____

_____

_____

_____

Read the question below. Your answer should be based on your own experience. Write complete sentences for your answer.

Personal Response Is the topic of the universe mostly _interesting_ or mostly _overwhelming_ to you? Support your answer with details from the passage.

_____

_____

_____

_____

_____

The Universe (continued)

Grammar, Usage, and Mechanics

Read each question. Fill in the bubble beside the answer in each group that is correct. If none of the answers is correct, choose the last answer, "none of the above."

1. In which sentence is a demonstrative pronoun underlined?

Ⓐ A bag of groceries was on <u>the</u> table.

Ⓑ <u>This</u> box was on the porch.

Ⓒ Dad found <u>these</u> in the attic.

Ⓓ none of the above

2. In which sentence is a demonstrative pronoun underlined?

Ⓐ <u>Those</u> trees turn red in the fall.

Ⓑ A big fish lives in <u>that</u> pond.

Ⓒ When you see <u>them</u>, be sure to say hello.

Ⓓ none of the above

3. Which sentence contains a demonstrative pronoun?

Ⓐ Put that away. Ⓒ She likes red socks.

Ⓑ Those boots are muddy. Ⓓ none of the above

4. Which sentence has correct punctuation?

Ⓐ The next town is thir-teen miles away.

Ⓑ September has thirty-days.

Ⓒ The bus left at fourfifteen.

Ⓓ none of the above

5. Which sentence has a mistake in punctuation?

Ⓐ The family stayed in an old-fashioned inn.

Ⓑ The temperature dropped below thirty two-degrees

Ⓒ A hard-working team cleaned up the park.

Ⓓ none of the above

The Universe (continued)

Analyzing the Selection

Read the questions below. Write complete sentences for your answer. Support your answer with information from the selection.

How has reading this selection changed your understanding of the universe? What are some other things about the universe that you would like to learn more about?

_____

_____

_____

_____

_____

_____

_____

_____

_____

_____

_____

The Universe (continued)

Oral Fluency Assessment

Raccoons

The raccoon is a funny looking creature that is found in many parts of the United States. It is mostly gray with a long, striped tail. A patch of black hair around a raccoon's eyes looks like a bandit's mask. Because of its unusual appearance, a raccoon is a favorite subject of cartoon artists.

Raccoons are mammals. Their young are born alive, and they get milk from their mothers. Raccoons will eat almost anything. Their favorite foods are fish, crayfish, frogs, and turtles. They will catch mice and will eat insects, nuts, fruits, and eggs. Farmers consider raccoons pests. They eat chickens' eggs and farm crops, especially corn.

A raccoon's hands are very much like a monkey's hands. They can hold things and can even turn a handle to open a door. Raccoons like to pick up their food and wash it before eating it. This is why they like to live near water, such as a river or stream.

Raccoon babies are born blind. They will stay in the den, usually in a hollow tree, for several weeks. When they get a little older, the mother teaches them to hunt and to climb trees. Raccoons look cuddly because of their soft fur. They are fierce fighters, however, especially when they are protecting their young.

Name _____ Date _____ Score _____

Circles, Squares, and Daggers

Vocabulary

Read each item. Fill in the bubble for the answer you think is correct.

1. The suffix **-tion** tells you that a word is a

Ⓐ adverb.　　　　Ⓒ verb.

Ⓑ noun.　　　　Ⓓ adjective.

2. Another word for **dramatic** is

Ⓐ exciting.　　　　Ⓒ secret.

Ⓑ dangerous.　　　　Ⓓ hopeful.

3. The Mayas and the ancient Egyptians were **stargazers.** The word **stargazers** means people who

Ⓐ tell stories about the stars.

Ⓑ attempt to travel to the stars.

Ⓒ look at and study the stars.

Ⓓ create art that features stars.

4. The slabs of stone lean against a **vertical** rock face. If something is **vertical**, it is

Ⓐ straight up and down.

Ⓑ jagged and rough.

Ⓒ filled with holes.

Ⓓ flat and smooth.

5. Native Americans relied on **solar** events to help determine when to plant. The word **solar** means

Ⓐ personal or private.　　　　Ⓒ traditional or sacred.

Ⓑ annual.　　　　Ⓓ related to the sun.

Circles, Squares, and Daggers (continued)

Comprehension

Read the following questions carefully. Then completely fill in the bubble of each correct answer. You may look back at the selection to find the answer to each of the questions.

1. The Bighorn and Cahokia observatories are both

   Ⓐ made from stones.

   Ⓑ over one thousand years old.

   Ⓒ circular in shape.

   Ⓓ located in Montana.

2. Why is the sunlight at the Fajada Butte observatory called a "dagger"?

   Ⓐ It is able to cut rock.

   Ⓑ It is shaped like a knife.

   Ⓒ It is painfully hot.

   Ⓓ It is used as a weapon.

Circles, Squares, and Daggers (continued)

3. To determine how the Cahokia observatory worked, archaeologists had to

   Ⓐ interview local people.

   Ⓑ use a new calendar.

   Ⓒ do research in the summer.

   Ⓓ rebuild part of the site.

4. Which of these is an opinion, not a fact?

   Ⓐ Archaeoastronomy is a very exciting new field.

   Ⓑ Archaeoastronomy combines both archaeology and astronomy.

   Ⓒ Archaeoastronomy is the study of ancient observatories.

   Ⓓ Archaeoastronomy shows how people of the past observed the skies.

5. The Moose Mountain Medicine Wheel, Casa Grande, and Hovenweep Castle are all

   Ⓐ "sun rooms."

   Ⓑ cairns.

   Ⓒ observatories.

   Ⓓ ceremonies.

Circles, Squares, and Daggers (continued)

Read the following questions carefully. Use complete sentences to answer the questions.

6. What are some of the reasons Native Americans studied astronomy?

_____

_____

_____

7. Other than being Anasazi structures, how are the Casa Grande and Hovenweep alike?

_____

_____

8. How was the Chaco Canyon observatory discovered?

_____

_____

9. In the following passage from the selection, what is opinion and what is fact? "The Anasazi . . . lived in the beautiful but dry country of northern New Mexico, Colorado, Utah, and Arizona around 900 years ago."

_____

_____

10. Why does the author say that the skies were the Native Americans' calendar?

_____

_____

Circles, Squares, and Daggers (continued)

Read the question below. Write complete sentences for your answer. Support your answer with information from the selection.

Linking to the Concepts What was the connection between early Native American observatories and important tribal ceremonies?

_____

_____

_____

_____

_____

_____

Read the question below. Your answer should be based on your own experience. Write complete sentences for your answer.

Personal Response Which of the observatories would you most like to visit? Support your answer with details from the selection.

_____

_____

_____

_____

_____

_____

Circles, Squares, and Daggers (continued)

Grammar, Usage, and Mechanics

Read each question. Fill in the bubble beside the answer in each group that is correct. If none of the answers is correct, choose the last answer, "none of the above."

1. What are the <u>margins</u> of a word-processing document?
   - Ⓐ the space between lines
   - Ⓑ the page breaks
   - Ⓒ the left and right sides
   - Ⓓ none of the above

2. What are <u>tabs</u> used for most often?
   - Ⓐ to make words more obvious
   - Ⓑ to indent paragraphs
   - Ⓒ to change the size of print
   - Ⓓ none of the above

3. Where is the <u>header</u> of a document found?
   - Ⓐ at the top
   - Ⓒ at the end
   - Ⓑ at the bottom
   - Ⓓ none of the above

4. What is the <u>format</u> of a word-processing document?
   - Ⓐ who will read it
   - Ⓑ the way it looks
   - Ⓒ what it is about
   - Ⓓ none of the above

5. Which of these would usually be found in a <u>header</u>?
   - Ⓐ the mistakes in a document
   - Ⓑ the important ideas in a document
   - Ⓒ the page numbers in the document
   - Ⓓ none of the above

Circles, Squares, and Daggers (continued)

Analyzing the Selection

Read the question below. Write complete sentences for your answer. Support your answer with information from the selection.

What important things can archaeoastronomy teach us today?

_____

_____

_____

_____

_____

_____

_____

_____

_____

_____

_____

Circles, Squares, and Daggers (continued)

Oral Fluency Assessment

On Top of the World

Sir Edmund Hillary was born in New Zealand in 1919. No one could imagine his future. The Queen of England would someday knight him. Here is the story of how the young boy grew to be a great adventurer.

Edmund first tried mountain climbing on a school trip. He loved climbing right away. He climbed the local mountains whenever he could. In order to climb safely, a person must be strong and reliable. Edmund was both. By the time he was in his twenties, he was known for his climbing.

The young climber then decided to try some mountains in Europe. Through his adventures there, he met Sir John Hunt. Hunt was planning a trip to Mount Everest. It was the highest mountain on Earth. It had never been scaled.

Hunt invited Edmund to go along on the trip. The result was history. On May 29, 1953, Edmund and his Nepalese guide, Tenzing Norgay, were the first people to reach the top of the world's tallest mountain.

Hillary never forgot the people of Nepal who helped him. For years, he has raised money for schools and hospitals. He is now recognized for his climbing and his kindness.

Name _____ Date _____ Score _____

The Mystery of Mars

Vocabulary

Read each item. Fill in the bubble for the answer you think is correct.

1. **Harsh** means about the same as

   Ⓐ dusty.   Ⓒ long.

   Ⓑ bright.   Ⓓ severe.

2. What is the meaning of the prefix *inter-?*

   Ⓐ between   Ⓒ without

   Ⓑ from   Ⓓ before

3. Scientists wondered if there might be **microscopic** life on the surface. Something **microscopic** is

   Ⓐ very friendly.   Ⓒ very small.

   Ⓑ very intelligent. Ⓓ very old.

4. The dry, dusty world did not look **hospitable. Hospitable** means

   Ⓐ healthy.

   Ⓑ rocky.

   Ⓒ inhabited.

   Ⓓ welcoming.

5. The robot needed to **analyze** the dirt. If you **analyze** something, you

   Ⓐ collect it in large numbers.

   Ⓑ find out what it is made of.

   Ⓒ push aside.

   Ⓓ put it back together.

The Mystery of Mars (continued)

Comprehension

Read the following questions carefully. Then completely fill in the bubble of each correct answer. You may look back at the selection to find the answer to each of the questions.

1. Which of these is an opinion?

   (A) Rain never falls on Mars.

   (B) There are sand dunes on Mars.

   (C) Winters on Mars are so cold that part of the air freezes.

   (D) The pink sky on Mars is prettier than Earth's sky.

2. This selection is mostly about

   (A) the differences between Mars and Earth.

   (B) what makes Mars mysterious.

   (C) the exploration of Mars.

   (D) why Mars has red soil.

The Mystery of Mars (continued)

3. On Earth, carbon dioxide and oxygen are normally both

Ⓐ forms of water.

Ⓑ gases.

Ⓒ types of dirt.

Ⓓ minerals.

4. Which of these statements is true?

Ⓐ Earth revolves around the sun and Mars does not.

Ⓑ Mars is a planet and Earth is not.

Ⓒ Earth has liquid water and Mars does not.

Ⓓ Mars is a solid planet and Earth is not.

5. Scientists suspect that no organic molecules have been found on Mars because

Ⓐ chemicals in the Martian soil destroy them.

Ⓑ solar winds blow them away.

Ⓒ Martian dust covers the molecules.

Ⓓ sunlight causes the molecules to change.

The Mystery of Mars (continued)

Read the following questions carefully. Use complete sentences to answer the questions.

6. How is life on Earth protected from the extreme conditions in space?

_____

_____

7. Why did the scientists heat samples of soil from Mars?

_____

_____

8. How did the *Sojourner* move around?

_____

_____

9. Why was it important to guide the *Viking* and *Pathfinder* spacecrafts to gently rolling Martian plains for their landings?

_____

_____

10. What is missing from Mars that would make it habitable?

_____

_____

The Mystery of Mars (continued)

Read the question below. Write complete sentences for your answer. Support your answer with information from the selection.

Linking to the Concepts What might it mean if Mars was once surrounded by an atmosphere similar to Earth's atmosphere?

_____

_____

_____

_____

_____

Read the questions below. Your answer should be based on your own experience. Write complete sentences for your answer.

Personal Response What part of the selection was most impressive or amazing to you? Why?

_____

_____

_____

_____

_____

_____

The Mystery of Mars (continued)

Grammar, Usage, and Mechanics

Read each question. Fill in the bubble beside the answer in each group that is correct. If none of the answers is correct, choose the last answer, "none of the above."

1. In which sentence is the independent clause underlined?

Ⓐ A cat sat on the floor <u>where the sun was shining</u>.

Ⓑ <u>A cat sat on the floor</u> where the sun was shining.

Ⓒ A cat sat on <u>the floor where the sun</u> was shining.

Ⓓ none of the above

2. In which sentence is the dependent clause underlined?

Ⓐ <u>Although it is small</u>, this park has many visitors.

Ⓑ Although it is small, <u>this park has many visitors</u>.

Ⓒ Although <u>it is small, this park</u> has many visitors.

Ⓓ none of the above

3. Which sentence includes a dependent clause?

Ⓐ The phone kept ringing.　Ⓒ Something is wrong.

Ⓑ No one answered it.　　Ⓓ none of the above

4. Which answer is a complex sentence?

Ⓐ A hawk flew across the valley.

Ⓑ The creek was beautiful, so the hikers took a break.

Ⓒ A coyote wandered through the forest.

Ⓓ none of the above

5. Which answer has two independent clauses?

Ⓐ The book was good, but the movie seemed dull.

Ⓑ Although the town is small, it has a great museum.

Ⓒ The beach becomes crowded on the weekend.

Ⓓ none of the above

The Mystery of Mars (continued)

Analyzing the Selection

Read the questions below. Write complete sentences for your answer. Support your answer with information from the selections.

Based on what you have read so far in the unit, how has our understanding of the universe changed over time? Do you think that such great changes will continue in the future? Why or why not?

_____

_____

_____

_____

_____

_____

_____

_____

_____

_____

_____

_____

The Mystery of Mars (continued)

Oral Fluency Assessment

Plimoth Plantation

If you ever visit the coast of Cape Cod, you might see an odd sight. On the shores of the Atlantic Ocean is a tiny town. The houses there look strange. The people wear funny clothes. If you ask the people questions, they will tell you all about their lives. They act as if it is 1627!

No, you have not traveled into the past. This place is called Plimoth Plantation. This is the same Plymouth where the Pilgrims landed. Everybody has heard about the Pilgrims. They came to America in 1620. They landed in what is now Massachusetts. They made friends with the Native Americans and established the tradition we now call Thanksgiving.

The Plimoth Plantation that sits on the Cape Cod shore is a living history museum. There are no glass cases in this museum. There are no security guards. There are no paintings. There are no tour guides. You can touch things in this museum, and the exhibits talk to you.

Some people think history is boring. So historians got an idea. Forget stuffy museums, they said. We should build a village just like the Pilgrims lived in. People can see what their life was like.

Name _____ Date _____ Score _____

Apollo 11: First Moon Landing

Vocabulary

Read each item. Fill in the bubble for the answer you think is correct.

1. Which word means the opposite of **bulky?**

   Ⓐ warm   Ⓒ tiny

   Ⓑ broken   Ⓓ fast

2. Sensations are

   Ⓐ challenges.   Ⓒ radio waves.

   Ⓑ feelings.   Ⓓ moon rocks.

3. When a rocket takes off, there is a great **thrust.** A **thrust** is a

   Ⓐ low rumble.

   Ⓑ bright flash.

   Ⓒ loud sound.

   Ⓓ strong force.

4. A **hatch** is part of a ship or spacecraft. What is a **hatch?**

   Ⓐ a type of opening

   Ⓑ a type of fin or rudder

   Ⓒ a small engine

   Ⓓ a landing device

5. The moon landing gave many people a sense of **awe. Awe** means

   Ⓐ responsibility.

   Ⓑ anger.

   Ⓒ wonder.

   Ⓓ doubt.

Apollo 11: First Moon Landing (continued)

Comprehension

Read the following questions carefully. Then completely fill in the bubble of each correct answer. You may look back at the selection to find the answer to each of the questions.

1. Which of these is an opinion?

    Ⓐ Neil Armstrong was the mission commander.

    Ⓑ The Moon landing was the most important exploration in history.

    Ⓒ When the astronauts returned to Earth, they were greeted as heroes.

    Ⓓ Astronaut Collins inspected the lunar module for damage.

2. What is the main idea of this selection?

    Ⓐ The first Moon landing was an important and dangerous trip.

    Ⓑ Mission Control kept in almost constant contact with Apollo 11.

    Ⓒ It took several hours for the men to put on their space suits.

    Ⓓ People all over the world watched the Moon landing.

Apollo 11: First Moon Landing (continued)

3. Why were many people left speechless by the sight of a man on the Moon?

Ⓐ They were angry it had taken so long.

Ⓑ They were disappointed by the quality of the images.

Ⓒ They were not sure what they were seeing.

Ⓓ They were awed by the accomplishment.

4. Where did the *Apollo 11* land when it returned to Earth?

Ⓐ in a large lake in Florida

Ⓑ in the Sea of Tranquility

Ⓒ in the Pacific Ocean

Ⓓ in the Atlantic Ocean

5. Why did the astronauts have their shortest rest period the day before the Moon landing?

Ⓐ They were too excited to sleep.

Ⓑ They were on a tight schedule.

Ⓒ They had to deal with the radio blackout.

Ⓓ They needed to fix the hatch.

Apollo 11: First Moon Landing (continued)

Read the following questions carefully. Use complete sentences to answer the questions.

6. What happened right after *Apollo 11* passed behind the dark side of the Moon?

_____

_____

7. Why did Armstrong say, "The *Eagle* has wings"?

_____

_____

8. Why was the Sea of Tranquility chosen for the *Eagle's* landing site?

_____

_____

9. Why was the astronauts' success so important?

_____

_____

10. Why did Mission Control tell the astronauts, "You've got a bunch of guys about to turn blue"?

_____

_____

Apollo 11: First Moon Landing (continued)

Read the question below. Write complete sentences for your answer. Support your answer with information from the selection.

Linking to the Concepts Why did Aldrin tell Congress that the footprints on the Moon belonged to the American people?

_____

_____

_____

_____

_____

Read the questions below. Your answer should be based on your own experience. Write complete sentences for your answer.

Personal Response If you could go where no human had gone before, would you? Why or why not?

_____

_____

_____

_____

_____

Apollo 11: First Moon Landing (continued)

Grammar, Usage, and Mechanics

Read each question. Fill in the bubble beside the answer in each group that is correct. If none of the answers is correct, choose the last answer, "none of the above."

1. Which of these is a sentence fragment?

 Ⓐ Almost no one there.   Ⓒ It was snowing.

 Ⓑ The city expected crowds.   Ⓓ none of the above

2. Which of these is a run-on sentence?

 Ⓐ The space shuttle normally lands in Florida.

 Ⓑ Weather is bad in other places.

 Ⓒ The shuttle must be flown back to the Space Center.

 Ⓓ none of the above

3. In which sentence do the subject and verb agree?

 Ⓐ A few geese lives there all year.

 Ⓑ A group of people stood under the awning.

 Ⓒ The chairs on the deck gets wet in a storm.

 Ⓓ none of the above

4. Which sentence has a mistake in subject-verb agreement?

 Ⓐ A box of toys were loaded into the car.

 Ⓑ Local families donate money to the shelter.

 Ⓒ The workers at the shelter care for many people.

 Ⓓ none of the above

5. Which sentence has correct punctuation?

 Ⓐ The truck didn't have enough gas for the trip.

 Ⓑ "We'll get some in a few minutes said the driver."

 Ⓒ The trucks tank hold's fifty gallons of gas.

 Ⓓ none of the above

Apollo 11: First Moon Landing (continued)

Analyzing the Selection

Read the questions below. Write complete sentences for your answer. Support your answer with information from the selection.

The United States has not landed a person on the Moon in many years. How important do you think it is to continue exploration using astronauts? Are the risks involved worth what is gained?

_____

_____

_____

_____

_____

_____

_____

_____

_____

_____

_____

_____

Apollo 11: First Moon Landing (continued)

Oral Fluency Assessment

Our Strange Geography

Most people think that sand dunes are only on beaches. The Great Sand Dunes National Monument, however, is in Colorado. It is at the foot of the Rocky Mountains. That is a thousand miles from the nearest ocean. Wind and weather have created great sand dunes there. The area is not far from some of the best skiing in the United States.

Speaking of skiing, Taos Ski Valley is known for its steep slopes and perfect snow. This beautiful resort is located in a state we think of as being hot and dry. That state is New Mexico.

Canada and Mexico share a border with the United States. They are our closest neighbors. The next closest is Russia. Parts of Russia are less than a mile from Alaska. Speaking of Alaska, our largest state stretches across four time zones. The rules have been bent a little. Just one time zone is used for the whole state.

About a third of Michigan is separated from the rest of the state. That area is called the Upper Peninsula. The region is actually connected to Wisconsin.

What strange geography do you have in your home state?

Name _____ Date _____ Score _____

Ellen Ochoa: Reaching for the Stars

Vocabulary

Read each item. Fill in the bubble for the answer you think is correct.

1. The Greek root **graph** means about the same as
   - Ⓐ to read.
   - Ⓒ to speak.
   - Ⓑ to run.
   - Ⓓ to write.

2. Another word for **precise** is
   - Ⓐ exact.
   - Ⓒ quick.
   - Ⓑ sloppy.
   - Ⓓ new.

3. Today Ochoa works to **advance** space exploration. In this sentence, **advance** means
   - Ⓐ to try to find something.
   - Ⓑ to finish doing something.
   - Ⓒ to help the progress of something.
   - Ⓓ to point out problems with something.

4. To carry out these important missions takes **confidence.** **Confidence** is
   - Ⓐ years of study.
   - Ⓑ faith in oneself.
   - Ⓒ support from others.
   - Ⓓ willingness to practice.

5. Ochoa waited to hear about her **application** with NASA. An **application** is a type of
   - Ⓐ mission.
   - Ⓒ request.
   - Ⓑ teacher.
   - Ⓓ job.

Ellen Ochoa: Reaching for the Stars (continued)

Comprehension

Read the following questions carefully. Then completely fill in the bubble of each correct answer. You may look back at the selection to find the answer to each of the questions.

1. On her first mission to space, Ochoa

Ⓐ helped to install a truss at the ISS.

Ⓑ gathered information about the ozone.

Ⓒ retrieved a satellite using the robot arm.

Ⓓ transferred supplies to the crew of the ISS.

2. When did Ochoa decide to become an astronaut?

Ⓐ while watching the first moon landing on television

Ⓑ when she heard about a Russian female cosmonaut

Ⓒ after getting her Ph.D. from Stanford

Ⓓ after moving near the Johnson Space Center

Ellen Ochoa • **Lesson Assessment Book 2**

Ellen Ochoa: Reaching for the Stars (continued)

3. Based on the information in the selection, you can infer that Ochoa

   Ⓐ was a dedicated student.

   Ⓑ saw humor in everyday things.

   Ⓒ was a promising athlete.

   Ⓓ enjoyed music most of all.

4. Why did a professor discourage Ochoa from pursuing an engineering career?

   Ⓐ The professor thought that her work was below standard.

   Ⓑ The professor suspected that engineering was a dying field.

   Ⓒ The professor saw that she liked other subjects more.

   Ⓓ The professor believed that engineering was for men.

5. Which of these probably most influenced Ochoa to apply at NASA?

   Ⓐ having a mother for a strong role model

   Ⓑ knowing that other women had been hired

   Ⓒ being honored by her middle school teachers

   Ⓓ knowing the job carried a potential for danger

Ellen Ochoa: Reaching for the Stars (continued)

Read the following questions carefully. Use complete sentences to answer the questions.

6. List two jobs, in the order that Ochoa did them, using the "robot arm."

_____

_____

_____

7. How does Ochoa work "to make life better for everyone else"?

_____

_____

8. What types of supplies does Ochoa transfer to the ISS?

_____

_____

9. How is the RMS or robot arm like a real arm?

_____

_____

10. According to Ochoa, why is the ISS important?

_____

_____

Ellen Ochoa: Reaching for the Stars (continued)

Read the question below. Write complete sentences for your answer. Support your answer with information from the selection.

Linking to the Concepts What might Ochoa's example communicate to young girls of today?

_____

_____

_____

_____

_____

Read the question below. Your answer should be based on your own experience. Write complete sentences for your answer.

Personal Response If you could have any career you wanted, what would that career be? Explain your choice.

_____

_____

_____

_____

_____

_____

Ellen Ochoa: Reaching for the Stars (continued)

Grammar, Usage, and Mechanics

Read each question. Fill in the bubble beside the answer in each group that is correct. If none of the answers is correct, choose the last answer, "none of the above."

1. Which sentence contains a demonstrative pronoun?

   Ⓐ When will you be going to the post office?

   Ⓑ These letters do not have stamps on them.

   Ⓒ The delivery service left that on the porch.

   Ⓓ none of the above

2. Which sentence has a singular demonstrative pronoun?

   Ⓐ Please hand this to grandmother.

   Ⓑ Those can be recycled.

   Ⓒ Put these in a brown paper bag.

   Ⓓ none of the above

3. Which sentence is correct?

   Ⓐ Rake that part of the garden, she said.

   Ⓑ "I'll get Jake's things," Dad said.

   Ⓒ "Theyre next to the door I said."

   Ⓓ none of the above

4. Which of these is a sentence fragment?

   Ⓐ Jason started late.　　Ⓒ Our seats are near here.

   Ⓑ Meet us at the game.　　Ⓓ none of the above

5. Which sentence is correct?

   Ⓐ The wood for the fires are stacked beside the garage.

   Ⓑ The fireplace is nice we use it on cold nights.

   Ⓒ Reading in front of the fire is wonderful.

   Ⓓ none of the above

Ellen Ochoa: Reaching for the Stars (continued)

Analyzing the Selection

Read the questions below. Write complete sentences for your answer. Support your answer with information from the selections.

What types of abilities and interests do scientists and astronauts share? How are they similar, and how are they different?

_____

_____

_____

_____

_____

_____

_____

_____

_____

_____

_____

_____

Ellen Ochoa: Reaching for the Stars (continued)

Oral Fluency Assessment

Redwood Trees

Every part of the country has a special tree that is native to that region. On the northwest coast of the United States, the special tree is the redwood. These tall, reddish-brown trees grow in beautiful forests. They usually grow near the ocean. Redwood trees need a great deal of moisture. Being near the ocean provides them with ample exposure to rain and fog.

Redwoods grow to be very old. Some live for hundreds of years. Scientists know the age of these trees by looking at their growth rings. If a redwood tree is cut crossways, you can see these rings. A ring is formed for each year of a tree's life. Researchers study redwood tree rings to learn the age of the tree and what the climate and environmental conditions were like in the forest as the tree was growing.

The tallest trees on record are redwoods. For example, the Rockefeller Tree, a redwood, is three hundred and sixty-seven feet high. It is the tallest tree in the world. If you were to put this tree on a football field, it would reach all the way from one goalpost to the other.

Ellen Ochoa • **Lesson Assessment Book 2**

Name _____ Date _____ Score _____

Narrative Writing

Writing Situation
A spaceship flight

Audience
Your friends and family

Directions for Writing
Imagine that it is the future. Write a story about a group of students your age traveling to a planet outside our solar system. Describe the spaceship and what the students do on the trip.

Checklist
You will earn the best score if you
- think about your ideas and plan your writing before you begin.
- get the reader's attention with an exciting first paragraph.
- have a good beginning, middle, and end to your story.
- make sure your ideas flow in a way that makes sense.
- use sensory words and figurative language so the reader can experience the story.
- tell about the characters in your story.
- provide details so the reader can understand the setting.
- relate the setting to the plot of the story.
- describe the problem and solution that are the basis of the plot of the story.
- tell events in the order they happen.

Buffalo Hunt

Vocabulary

Read each item. Fill in the bubble for the answer you think is correct.

1. **Lurking** means about the same as
   - Ⓐ laughing.
   - Ⓒ jumping.
   - Ⓑ preparing.
   - Ⓓ hiding.

2. Which Latin root means "to speak"?
   - Ⓐ *form*
   - Ⓒ *tact*
   - Ⓑ *dict*
   - Ⓓ *script*

3. The buffalo hunters formed a grand **procession.**
   A **procession** is
   - Ⓐ a meal of great celebration.
   - Ⓑ a gathering place on the prairie.
   - Ⓒ a line of people moving forward.
   - Ⓓ a place of honor for the leaders.

4. Hunters would sometimes **stampede** the buffalo over cliffs. In this sentence, **stampede** means to
   - Ⓐ sneak up on a herd quietly.
   - Ⓑ observe a herd from a distance.
   - Ⓒ distract a herd with loud noises.
   - Ⓓ cause a herd to run wildly.

5. They **pitched** their tipis along the canyon floor. In this sentence, **pitched** means they
   - Ⓐ repaired their tipis.
   - Ⓒ connected their tipis.
   - Ⓑ set up their tipis.
   - Ⓓ left their tipis behind.

Buffalo Hunt (continued)

Comprehension

Read the following questions carefully. Then completely fill in the bubble of each correct answer. You may look back at the selection to find the answer to each of the questions.

1. Having so many buffalo legends shows that Plains Indians

   (A) wanted to warn others about the buffalo.

   (B) placed great importance on the buffalo.

   (C) believed the buffalo was their creation.

   (D) viewed the buffalo as a storyteller.

2. The Comanche and Blackfoot buffalo legends differ in

   (A) what the buffalo look like.

   (B) how important the buffalo are.

   (C) where the buffalo come from.

   (D) how the buffalo are used.

Buffalo Hunt (continued)

3. On the day of a hunt, the first thing the hunters did was

Ⓐ send out the scouts.

Ⓑ eat a quick meal.

Ⓒ pack up the camp.

Ⓓ gather for a discussion.

4. Why was it important for everyone to be quiet during a hunt?

Ⓐ The buffalo could hear weak and far off sounds.

Ⓑ The hunters had to concentrate on the herd.

Ⓒ The hunt was a sacred act with rites and ceremonies.

Ⓓ The buffalo made a special sound.

5. Much of the buffalo meat was made into jerky because it was

Ⓐ a popular snack with traders.

Ⓑ an easy recipe to make.

Ⓒ a tough meat to chew.

Ⓓ a way to preserve the meat.

Buffalo Hunt (continued)

Read the following questions carefully. Use complete sentences to answer the questions.

6. How did the arrival of horses change buffalo hunting?

_____

_____

_____

7. How did men's and women's responsibilities differ during a hunt?

_____

_____

8. How was the scout's job different from the marshal's job?

_____

_____

9. Why are the artists' paintings of buffalo hunts helpful to us today?

_____

_____

10. What were some of the things that buffalo hides were useful for?

_____

_____

Buffalo Hunt (continued)

Read the question below. Write complete sentences for your answer. Support your answer with information from the selection.

Linking to the Concepts How did the arrival of white settlers affect the buffalo hunt?

_____

_____

_____

_____

_____

Read the question below. Your answer should be based on your own experience. Write complete sentences for your answer.

Personal Response Is there a difference between killing buffalo for survival and killing buffalo for profit? Support your opinion with details from the selection.

_____

_____

_____

_____

_____

_____

Buffalo Hunt (continued)

Grammar, Usage, and Mechanics

Read each question. Fill in the bubble beside the answer in each group that is correct. If none of the answers is correct, choose the last answer, "none of the above."

1. Which sentence contains an appositive?

Ⓐ The group took a walk through a nature preserve.

Ⓑ Several birds flew by, but no one knew what they were.

Ⓒ The animal, a type of rabbit, hopped into the bushes.

Ⓓ none of the above

2. Which sentence has a mistake in punctuation?

Ⓐ The snow was great, and the resort was perfect.

Ⓑ People enjoy different types of vacations.

Ⓒ The cruise was on a huge ship the *KIWI 5*.

Ⓓ none of the above

3. Which sentence is in the past tense?

Ⓐ The fish swim in a tank. Ⓒ The dog chased a ball.

Ⓑ A cat was chasing birds. Ⓓ none of the above

4. Which sentence is in the present perfect tense?

Ⓐ Rachel misplaced her backpack.

Ⓑ She had carried it with her to school.

Ⓒ Her friend found it behind a pile of books.

Ⓓ none of the above

5. Which sentence is in the future tense?

Ⓐ All the players practiced hard for the game.

Ⓑ The coaches make sure the players do their homework.

Ⓒ The team will travel to the game on a bus.

Ⓓ none of the above

Buffalo Hunt (continued)

Analyzing the Selection

Read the questions below. Write complete sentences for your answer. Support your answer with information from the selection.

What would have happened if the buffalo had not disappeared? Would Native Americans still have kept the old ways?

_____

_____

_____

_____

_____

_____

_____

_____

_____

_____

_____

_____

_____

Buffalo Hunt (continued)

Oral Fluency Assessment

Candy for Your Health

If you had a sore throat many years ago, your doctor might have given you candy. Your candy "cure" would have been a small, yellow root. It was the root of a licorice plant.

For over three thousand years, people have known about the benefits of licorice. Licorice is a flowering shrub that grows to about four to five feet tall. The root of the plant is very sweet. In fact, it is about fifty times sweeter than sugar!

To make the black, whip-like candy that we call licorice, the roots from the plant are ground up and boiled. When the water evaporates, a liquid called extract is left behind. This extract can be used as a flavoring. And the flavor of licorice is used in candy, tea, soft drinks, and even medicines.

Taste is not the only reason it is used in medicines. Licorice has healing powers. It is known to build strength, to fight stress, to ease pain, and even to stop coughs and sore throats. A recent study suggests that licorice may even help stop the growth of some cancers.

So the next time you have a sore throat, get to the root of the matter. Do as the doctor ordered. Try some good old-fashioned licorice!

Name _____ Date _____ Score _____

The Journal of Wong Ming-Chung

Vocabulary

Read each item. Fill in the bubble for the answer you think is correct.

1. What is the meaning of the suffix **-ent?**
   - Ⓐ made of
   - Ⓑ full of
   - Ⓒ having the quality of
   - Ⓓ without

2. If something is **raggedy,** it is
   - Ⓐ worn out.
   - Ⓑ old-fashioned.
   - Ⓒ new.
   - Ⓓ expensive.

3. When food is **rationed,** it is
   - Ⓐ cooked too much.
   - Ⓑ limited to small portions.
   - Ⓒ carried away to be eaten later.
   - Ⓓ tasteless and chewy.

4. Wong Ming-Chung and Uncle **registered** their claim. This means they
   - Ⓐ kept it a secret.
   - Ⓑ discovered it by accident.
   - Ⓒ sold it.
   - Ⓓ recorded it officially.

5. Wong Ming-Chung had a **theory** about the gold. What is a **theory?**
   - Ⓐ a way to find gold
   - Ⓑ a legend
   - Ⓒ an opinion based on evidence
   - Ⓓ a box in which gold could be kept

The Journal of Wong Ming-Chung (continued)

Comprehension

Read the following questions carefully. Then completely fill in the bubble of each correct answer. You may look back at the selection to find the answer to each of the questions.

1. What happens right after the rocker is built?

   (A) Wong Ming-Chung carries water in his hat.

   (B) Uncle digs up some soil.

   (C) Uncle gets discouraged.

   (D) Wong Ming-Chung runs his fingertips along the rocker's edge.

2. This selection is written from what point of view?

   (A) first-person point of view

   (B) second-person point of view

   (C) third-person point of view

   (D) Uncle's point of view

The Journal of Wong Ming-Chung (continued)

3. What happens last in the selection?

Ⓐ Wong Ming-Chung sneaks away to find Uncle.

Ⓑ Wong Ming-Chung tells Uncle his theory.

Ⓒ Wong Ming-Chung arrives in Sacramento.

Ⓓ Wong Ming-Chung has a nightmare about being chased by the mob.

4. When people ask Wong Ming-Chung and Uncle questions, they

Ⓐ introduce themselves.

Ⓑ answer proudly.

Ⓒ invent stories.

Ⓓ smile and say little.

5. What do Wong Ming-Chung and Uncle intend to send to China?

Ⓐ gold dust

Ⓑ money

Ⓒ mining supplies

Ⓓ letters of transit

The Journal of Wong Ming-Chung (continued)

Read the following questions carefully. Use complete sentences to answer the questions.

6. Why does the river look like a battlefield?

_____

_____

7. Why did Uncle say such hurtful things to Wong Ming-Chung?

_____

_____

8. Why do the Americans laugh at Wong Ming-Chung and Uncle when they register their claim?

_____

_____

9. Why do Wong Ming-Chung and Uncle go from abandoned claim to abandoned claim?

_____

_____

10. Why do Wong Ming-Chung and Uncle make themselves look dirty and shabby on their trip to Sacramento?

_____

_____

The Journal of Wong Ming-Chung (continued)

Read the question below. Write complete sentences for your answer. Support your answer with information from the selection.

Linking to the Concepts How do the actions of Wong Ming-Chung and Uncle show that they are clever?

_____

_____

_____

_____

_____

Read the prompt below. Your journal entry should be based on your own experience. Write complete sentences for your journal entry.

Personal Response Write a journal entry about something interesting that happened to you today. Try to include the same types of details that Wong Ming-Chung included in his journal.

_____

_____

_____

_____

_____

_____

The Journal of Wong Ming-Chung (continued)

Grammar, Usage, and Mechanics

Read each question. Fill in the bubble beside the answer in each group that is correct. If none of the answers is correct, choose the last answer, "none of the above."

1. In which sentence is the underlined word used incorrectly?

Ⓐ When there is lightning, <u>it's</u> better to stay inside.

Ⓑ I need to stop at <u>your</u> house for a moment.

Ⓒ Julie wanted <u>to</u> enter the ski race.

Ⓓ none of the above

2. In which sentence is the underlined word used incorrectly?

Ⓐ <u>Sit</u> that box on the table.

Ⓑ Do you have <u>their</u> phone number?

Ⓒ Carlos is taller <u>than</u> Patricia.

Ⓓ none of the above

3. In which sentence is the underlined word used incorrectly?

Ⓐ Dan wants to <u>buy</u> a new bicycle.

Ⓑ A piece <u>of</u> paper fell to the floor.

Ⓒ Please <u>rise</u> the window a few inches.

Ⓓ none of the above

4. In which sentence is the underlined word used incorrectly?

Ⓐ A big truck <u>passed</u> by the park.

Ⓑ <u>Lie</u> the wood next to the garage door.

Ⓒ Our team should <u>have</u> won the game.

Ⓓ none of the above

5. Which of these is an exclamatory sentence?

Ⓐ That dish is hot!　　　Ⓒ This soup smells good.

Ⓑ Would you like to eat?　　Ⓓ none of the above

The Journal of Wong Ming-Chung (continued)

Analyzing the Selection

Read the question below. Write complete sentences for your answer. Support your answer with information from the selection.

Why were success stories so important to the development of the American West? Use information from the selection, information you already know, and your opinion to write your response.

_____

_____

_____

_____

_____

_____

_____

_____

_____

_____

_____

_____

_____

The Journal of Wong Ming-Chung (continued)

Oral Fluency Assessment

Space Neighbors?

The next time you are outside on a clear night, look up. All those stars up there are suns. They are a lot like our own sun. Some are bigger than our sun, and some are smaller. A few are very, very old.

Once in a while, astronomers find a planet near one of these stars. So far, all of the planets have been cold and dead. But some scientists think that maybe there is a planet with life on it. And they want to communicate with that life.

Back in the 1950s, when your grandparents were young, NASA started a program to find life on other planets. It was called the Search for Extraterrestrial Intelligence (SETI). They did not use spaceships to find new life. They did not use transporters, jump gates, or other things you might see on television or in the movies. They used plain old radios!

The scientists who worked at the SETI Institute thought that any intelligent life probably knew about radio waves. Earth sends out billions of weak radio waves every day. They come from things like television broadcasts and satellites. Scientists figured that other life might have things like that, too. So they started watching space for certain types of radio waves.

Name _____ Date _____ Score _____

Bill Pickett: Rodeo-Ridin' Cowboy

Vocabulary

Read each item. Fill in the bubble for the answer you think is correct.

1. Which word best describes the following word relationship?

trip, expedition, voyage

Ⓐ schools   Ⓒ journeys

Ⓑ settlements   Ⓓ meetings

2. Another word for **trek** is

Ⓐ journey.   Ⓒ rope.

Ⓑ lesson.   Ⓓ wagon.

3. Bill performed his bulldogging **stunt** before a large rodeo crowd. In this sentence, **stunt** means a(n)

Ⓐ long speech.

Ⓑ act of skill or strength.

Ⓒ silly song.

Ⓓ dance move.

4. One of the cowboys gave the young Bill a **challenge.** A **challenge** is like a

Ⓐ chance to apologize for something.

Ⓑ new way of looking at something.

Ⓒ fight about something foolish.

Ⓓ dare to do something difficult.

5. Bill's father had helped others to grow **prospering** crops. **Prospering** means that the crops

Ⓐ were just sprouting.   Ⓒ grew year round.

Ⓑ did very well.   Ⓓ fed livestock.

Bill Pickett: Rodeo-Ridin' Cowboy (continued)

Comprehension

Read the following questions carefully. Then completely fill in the bubble of each correct answer. You may look back at the selection to find the answer to each of the questions.

1. Which statement about Pickett is an opinion?

Ⓐ He became a rodeo performer.

Ⓑ He grew up north of Austin, Texas.

Ⓒ He was the second of thirteen children.

Ⓓ He turned the 101 Ranch Wild West Show into a wonder.

2. Which statement expresses a fact?

Ⓐ Watching the bulldog was an eye-popping sight.

Ⓑ The songs made him more up-jumpy than ever.

Ⓒ Pickett set out when he was no more than fifteen.

Ⓓ Bill was the feistiest boy south of Abilene.

Bill Pickett: Rodeo-Ridin' Cowboy (continued)

3. Pickett's stunt was called "bulldoggin'" because he

Ⓐ performed it with a bulldog.

Ⓑ held the calf like the bulldog had done.

Ⓒ was as stubborn as a bulldog.

Ⓓ got down like a bulldog on all fours.

4. Saddling horses, mucking stalls, and lassoing steers are all

Ⓐ rodeo stunts.

Ⓑ riding tools.

Ⓒ tall tales.

Ⓓ cowhand jobs.

5. When Pickett was not performing, he was usually

Ⓐ telling stories about his rodeo feats.

Ⓑ keeping the old family ranch going.

Ⓒ helping cowboys do their branding.

Ⓓ teaching his children how to bulldog.

Bill Pickett: Rodeo-Ridin' Cowboy (continued)

Read the following questions carefully. Use complete sentences to answer the questions.

6. Why did the Millers approach Pickett and offer him a job?

_____

_____

7. What effect did traveling with the 101 Ranch Wild West Show have on Pickett's career?

_____

_____

8. Why did Pickett eventually give up performing with the 101 Ranch Wild West Show?

_____

_____

9. How is being a cowhand similar to being a rodeo performer? How is it different?

_____

_____

10. According to the selection, how did Pickett's bulldogging affect today's rodeo?

_____

_____

Bill Pickett: Rodeo-Ridin' Cowboy (continued)

Read the question below. Write complete sentences for your answer. Support your answer with information from the selection.

Linking to the Concepts In what ways is Pickett a hero of the West?

_____

_____

_____

_____

_____

Read the question below. Your answer should be based on your own experience. Write complete sentences for your answer.

Personal Response Have you ever done something that really impressed or surprised people? Write about what you did.

_____

_____

_____

_____

Bill Pickett: Rodeo-Ridin' Cowboy (continued)

Grammar, Usage, and Mechanics

Fill in the bubble beside the answer that is correct.

1. Which sentence has correct punctuation?

Ⓐ The knives, forks, and, spoons are in that drawer.

Ⓑ The knives forks, and spoons are in that drawer.

Ⓒ The knives, forks, and spoons are in that drawer.

Ⓓ none of the above

2. Which sentence has correct capitalization?

Ⓐ She shouted, "Don't dive into the water!"

Ⓑ She shouted, "don't dive into the water!"

Ⓒ She Shouted, "don't dive into the water!"

Ⓓ none of the above

3. Which sentence has correct punctuation?

Ⓐ It had three parks: Rye: Penn: and Salk.

Ⓑ It had three parks: Rye, Penn and Salk.

Ⓒ It had three parks: Rye, Penn, and Salk.

Ⓓ none of the above

4. Which sentence has correct punctuation?

Ⓐ The cookout was fun; the whole family was there.

Ⓑ The cookout was; fun the whole family was there.

Ⓒ The cookout was fun the whole family; was there.

Ⓓ none of the above

5. Which sentence has correct punctuation?

Ⓐ Because it is raining the game, will be canceled.

Ⓑ Because it is raining, the game will be canceled.

Ⓒ Because, it is raining, the game will be canceled.

Ⓓ none of the above

Bill Pickett: Rodeo-Ridin' Cowboy (continued)

Analyzing the Selection

Read the questions below. Write complete sentences for your answer. Support your answer with information from the selections.

Think about the three selections you have read in this unit. What are some common themes among them? What do these themes tell about the American West?

_____

_____

_____

_____

_____

_____

_____

_____

_____

_____

_____

_____

_____

_____

Bill Pickett: Rodeo-Ridin' Cowboy (continued)

Oral Fluency Assessment

A Canal Boat Vacation

For Bill and his friends, it was a dream come true. They were about to begin a trip through the canals in France. They would travel on a boat that had seven cabins. It also had three bathrooms, a kitchen, a dining area, and a sitting room.

The students and their advisors had flown to France the day before. Today they would board their boat. The King School Boating Club had been planning the trip for a year. The students and their advisors had raised all the money themselves. So far, everything had gone perfectly. They could not wait to get started.

The idea for the trip had come from the club's advisors, Mr. and Mrs. Lesnik. They had taken a canal boat vacation a few years earlier and really enjoyed it. They thought the students would have a good time. In addition, they would learn more about the people, geography, and culture of another country.

The group included the Lesniks and ten club members. The students knew they were lucky to be going on such a special trip. They were excited about traveling overseas and seeing a country from the deck of a canal boat.

Name _____ Date _____ Score _____

Ghost Towns of the American West

Vocabulary

Read each item. Fill in the bubble for the answer you think is correct.

1. Which word fits in this base word family?

_____, **joyous, joyful, joyless**

Ⓐ excited   Ⓒ enjoyment

Ⓑ happiness   Ⓓ jolt

2. Another word for **evidence** is

Ⓐ mistake.   Ⓒ judgment.

Ⓑ trial.   Ⓓ proof.

3. Many settlers who came West **longed** for a better life. The word **longed** means

Ⓐ wanted something very much.

Ⓑ spent a lot of time on something.

Ⓒ wrote stories or songs about something.

Ⓓ wondered when something would happen.

4. Prospectors risked going into dangerous **territory.** A **territory** is

Ⓐ a deep mine.   Ⓒ a ghost town.

Ⓑ a region of land. Ⓓ a mountain pass.

5. Even the hopes and dreams of ghost town **inhabitants** have blown away. **Inhabitants** are those who

Ⓐ live in a certain place.

Ⓑ helped build a new town.

Ⓒ are constantly on the move.

Ⓓ relatives who came before you.

Ghost Towns of the American West (continued)

Comprehension

Read the following questions carefully. Then completely fill in the bubble of each correct answer. You may look back at the selection to find the answer to each of the questions.

1. Most ghost towns started out as

Ⓐ mining camps.

Ⓑ large cities.

Ⓒ railroad stations.

Ⓓ wagon trails.

2. Which of these was the typical Western town least likely to have?

Ⓐ sidewalks made of wood

Ⓑ hitching posts for horses

Ⓒ a blacksmith shop

Ⓓ a railroad station

Ghost Towns of the American West (continued)

3. According to the author, finding ghost towns today is as difficult as

   Ⓐ the wagon ride westward.

   Ⓑ the founding of a camp.

   Ⓒ the search for gold.

   Ⓓ the stagecoach route.

4. Why are quotes used in this selection?

   Ⓐ to show how people in the towns talked

   Ⓑ to include observations from that time period

   Ⓒ to share what today's experts think

   Ⓓ to include dialogue between the characters

5. Which of these statements is a fact?

   Ⓐ An air of mystery swirls around the ghost towns of the American West.

   Ⓑ Sad and joyous events happened within the tumbledown walls and streets.

   Ⓒ The Americans have a perfect passion for railroads.

   Ⓓ The waves of western migration reached a peak between 1860 and 1880.

Ghost Towns of the American West (continued)

Read the following questions carefully. Use complete sentences to answer the questions.

6. What are some of the reasons people came to settle in the lonesome West?

_____

_____

7. Why did some people abandon their settlements in the West?

_____

_____

8. According to the selection, the California gold rush attracted what types of men?

_____

_____

9. What effect did the railroad have on a Western town?

_____

_____

10. What are most ghost towns like today?

_____

_____

Ghost Towns of the American West (continued)

Read the question below. Write complete sentences for your answer. Support your answer with information from the selection.

Linking to the Concepts What are some possible reasons these western towns came to be known as "ghost towns"?

_____

_____

_____

_____

_____

Read the question below. Your answer should be based on your own experience. Write complete sentences for your answer.

Personal Response What might future researchers say about your neighborhood?

_____

_____

_____

_____

Ghost Towns of the American West (continued)

Grammar, Usage, and Mechanics

Read each question. Fill in the bubble beside the answer in each group that is correct. If none of the answers is correct, choose the last answer, "none of the above."

1. In which sentence is the underlined word a transition word?

Ⓐ I will light the candles before <u>everyone</u> arrives.

Ⓑ I will <u>light</u> the candles before everyone arrives.

Ⓒ I will light the candles <u>before</u> everyone arrives.

Ⓓ none of the above

2. Which underlined word is a transition word about time?

Ⓐ The cat hid <u>behind</u> him.   Ⓒ A bird flew <u>above</u> me.

Ⓑ The lamb left <u>outside</u>.   Ⓓ none of the above

3. Which underlined word is a transition word that compares?

Ⓐ Hikers <u>sometimes</u> write their names in this book.

Ⓑ This beach is <u>just as</u> nice as the other one.

Ⓒ <u>During</u> winter, people snowboard on this mountain.

Ⓓ none of the above

4. Which sentence contains a participial phrase?

Ⓐ My brother found a leather jacket.

Ⓑ Ms. Fuertes, our principal, is on vacation.

Ⓒ Carlos, saying little, left the stage.

Ⓓ none of the above

5. Which sentence contains a misplaced modifier?

Ⓐ Hiking up the trail, we saw rocks that were unusual.

Ⓑ Hiking up the trail, the rocks were unusual.

Ⓒ Hiking up the trail, we saw unusual rocks.

Ⓓ none of the above

Ghost Towns of the American West (continued)

Analyzing the Selection

Read the question below. Write complete sentences for your answer. Support your answer with information from the selection.

Suppose you and your friends came upon a ghost town. What would it be like, and what are some things you would do there?

_____

_____

_____

_____

_____

_____

_____

_____

_____

_____

_____

_____

_____

_____

Ghost Towns of the American West (continued)

Oral Fluency Assessment

An Expensive Poster

"It's not just any old poster, Mom," Joe insisted.

"It's a lot of money for a poster," Joe's mom replied. She was feeling just as upset as Joe.

They were talking about an ad Joe had seen in a magazine. It was for a poster of the famous dinosaur battle scene painted by Charles R. Knight. The original painting was in the New York Museum of Natural History. Joe had never seen the original, but there were copies of it in every one of his dinosaur books. It was his favorite image of his favorite dinosaurs.

The problem with getting this amazing poster (which was a massive forty inches by fifty inches on fabric) was the cost. If it cost ten dollars or so, it would not be a problem. Joe had that much in his savings. It was not, however, ten dollars. It was one hundred dollars. That was a lot of money for a fifth-grader.

"But, Mom," Joe continued," it's the best picture ever. You don't understand."

Joe's mother did not understand; he was right about that. She could not dream why anybody would spend a hundred dollars on a poster of dinosaurs.

She sighed, "We've gone over this a dozen times. If you really want that poster, then you're going to have to earn the money for it yourself."

Name _____ Date _____ Score _____

McBroom the Rainmaker

Vocabulary

Read each item. Fill in the bubble for the answer you think is correct.

1. The word **accurate** means

   Ⓐ correct.   Ⓒ friendly.

   Ⓑ quiet.   Ⓓ smart.

2. What is the Latin origin of the word *false*?

   Ⓐ *facil*   Ⓒ *falsus*

   Ⓑ *fabula*   Ⓓ *veritas*

3. As a farmer, McBroom must know how to **predict** the weather. To **predict** something means to

   Ⓐ work hard at it.   Ⓒ explain it.

   Ⓑ change it.   Ⓓ tell it beforehand.

4. McBroom began **sowing** seeds. **Sowing** means

   Ⓐ ordering seeds from a store.

   Ⓑ planting seeds in the ground.

   Ⓒ deciding which seeds to plant.

   Ⓓ loading seeds in a truck.

5. A **drought** is when

   Ⓐ there is little or no rain.

   Ⓑ it is time to plant your crops.

   Ⓒ there is a big harvest.

   Ⓓ there is too much rain.

McBroom the Rainmaker (continued)

Comprehension

Read the following questions carefully. Then completely fill in the bubble of each correct answer. You may look back at the selection to find the answer to each of the questions.

1. How do the mosquitoes save the farm from drought?

   Ⓐ They poke holes in the rain clouds.

   Ⓑ They help turn the beets into turnips.

   Ⓒ They put on a wonderful fireworks show.

   Ⓓ They cry hard enough to water the crops.

2. Why do the children have to teach the tadpoles to swim?

   Ⓐ The tadpoles are younger than the children.

   Ⓑ The tadpoles have lost their mothers.

   Ⓒ The tadpoles have never seen water.

   Ⓓ The tadpoles are about to become frogs.

McBroom the Rainmaker • **Lesson Assessment Book 2**

McBroom the Rainmaker (continued)

3. This selection is written from what point of view?

(A) first-person point of view

(B) second-person point of view

(C) third-person point of view

(D) a mosquito's point of view

4. Crops and livestock are both

(A) used for transportation.

(B) raised on a farm.

(C) harvested from the soil.

(D) planted from seed.

5. Which of these was the first sign of drought?

(A) the hens laid fried eggs

(B) the cow gave powdered milk

(C) the vegetable clocks started running slow

(D) the mosquitoes began whining

McBroom the Rainmaker (continued)

Read the following questions carefully. Use complete sentences to answer the questions.

6. How were the children able to tell time using vegetables?

_____

_____

7. Why does McBroom load up his wagons with topsoil?

_____

_____

8. Why do McBroom and his children sleep under chicken wire?

_____

_____

9. What parts of this selection make it a tall tale?

_____

_____

10. How were radish seeds used as fireworks?

_____

_____

McBroom the Rainmaker (continued)

Read the question below. Write complete sentences for your answer. Support your answer with information from the selection.

Linking to the Concepts In what ways is McBroom a creative thinker?

_____

_____

_____

_____

_____

Read the question below. Your answer should be based on your own experience. Write complete sentences for your answer.

Personal Response Is a story like this mostly funny to you or mostly silly? Use details from the selection to support your opinion.

_____

_____

_____

_____

_____

McBroom the Rainmaker (continued)

Grammar, Usage, and Mechanics

Read each question. Fill in the bubble beside the answer in each group that is correct. If none of the answers is correct, choose the last answer, "none of the above."

1. Which sentence is in the future perfect tense?

   Ⓐ The storm took everyone by surprise.

   Ⓑ The sun will have melted the snow by tomorrow.

   Ⓒ The snow is falling more heavily than before.

   Ⓓ none of the above

2. Which sentence is in the past perfect tense?

   Ⓐ Barb said she had climbed that mountain before.

   Ⓑ A guide will lead us along the trail.

   Ⓒ Bill made the arrangements months ago.

   Ⓓ none of the above

3. Which sentence is correct?

   Ⓐ She told us a story.

   Ⓑ Its about how she gone home.

   Ⓒ I forgot it's title.

   Ⓓ none of the above

4. Which sentence is correct?

   Ⓐ Sit the bag down.   Ⓒ I want two pages.

   Ⓑ Go set in the seat.   Ⓓ none of the above

5. Which sentence has a participial phrase?

   Ⓐ Racing down the field, Alice scored.

   Ⓑ Libby scrubbed and painted the deck.

   Ⓒ My sister, Brandy, is home.

   Ⓓ none of the above

McBroom the Rainmaker (continued)

Analyzing the Selection

Read the questions below. Write complete sentences for your answer. Support your answer with information from the selections.

"McBroom the Rainmaker" is a tall tale. Many of the true stories of the American West are equally amazing. Think about the other selections you read in this unit. What parts of the unit were amazing or difficult to believe? Why?

_____

_____

_____

_____

_____

_____

_____

_____

_____

_____

_____

_____

McBroom the Rainmaker (continued)

Oral Fluency Assessment

A Great Cowboy

Everyone has enjoyed stories and movies about the Old West. One of the best known stories is about cattle drives.

The ranchers in Texas had to move their cattle a long way to market or to the railroads. A group of cowboys made sure the cows traveled together. They also kept the cows safe.

Many of the early cowboys who drove the cattle were African American. One cowboy, Nate Love, lived all the adventures of the Old West. Later, he wrote a book about it.

Nate Love was born to a slave family. When he was fifteen, he ran away and got a job as a cowpuncher on a cattle drive. He made many trips from the ranches to the markets. In his book, he told of fighting off wild animals, terrible weather, and the other challenges of the Old West. The work was hard and dirty, but Nate enjoyed it.

Adventurers such as Nate Love supplied food to the rest of the country with their cattle drives. They also helped settle the West. And, especially in the case of this cowboy, they left behind a history of life on the range.

Expository Writing

Writing Situation

An event that took place in the American West

Audience

Students your age from a different country

Directions for Writing

Describe an event or character from the American West.
Write the description for a person your age from another
country who does not know much about the American West.
Include enough details so the reader will be able to visualize
the event or person.

Checklist

You will earn the best score if you

- think about the event and plan your writing before
  you begin.
- remember that the reader will not know much about the
  American West.
- use sensory words and figurative language so the reader
  can experience the person or event.
- provide details so the reader can understand the setting.
- write complete sentences and avoid fragments or run-ons.
- write more sentences and longer sentences when
  you revise.
- use subjects, verbs, and modifiers correctly.
- have a good beginning, middle, and end to your story.
- avoid words and phrases that are often overused.
- read your writing after you finish and check for mistakes.

Name _____ Date _____ Score _____

Founders of the Children's Rain Forest

Vocabulary

Read each item. Fill in the bubble for the answer you think is correct.

1. What is the meaning of the Greek root *bio?*

Ⓐ sun   Ⓒ land

Ⓑ water   Ⓓ life

2. A **macaw** is a type of

Ⓐ bear.   Ⓒ fish.

Ⓑ parrot.   Ⓓ forest.

3. The children asked for **donations** for the rain forest. **Donations** are

Ⓐ gifts or contributions.   Ⓒ trees to plant.

Ⓑ animals.   Ⓓ protective laws.

4. Rain forests are usually found in the **tropics.** What are **tropics?**

Ⓐ areas near the poles

Ⓑ land with lots of farms

Ⓒ areas near the equator

Ⓓ low mountain ranges

5. Many **species** live in the rain forest. **Species** are

Ⓐ native people.

Ⓑ groups of related plants or animals.

Ⓒ monkeys with short tails.

Ⓓ colorful birds.

Founders of the Children's Rain Forest (continued)

Comprehension

Read the following questions carefully. Then completely fill in the bubble of each correct answer. You may look back at the selection to find the answer to each of the questions.

1. The author wrote this selection to

Ⓐ convince people to visit a rain forest.

Ⓑ tell about an important project students did.

Ⓒ show why Sweden is such a nice place.

Ⓓ explain how to buy a rain forest.

2. The students wanted Mrs. Kern to

Ⓐ find a rain forest they could buy.

Ⓑ teach them how to earn money.

Ⓒ go on a field trip to the jungle.

Ⓓ tell them about other places they could save.

Founders of the Children's Rain Forest (continued)

3. The children were not afraid to ask for money because

    Ⓐ they knew they would not be refused.

    Ⓑ they already had more than they needed.

    Ⓒ they knew what they wanted to do with the money was important.

    Ⓓ they had asked Kinsman for permission to raise money.

4. The amount of money Fagervik students raised

    Ⓐ was not enough to buy any rain forest.

    Ⓑ was much more than they first expected.

    Ⓒ was only enough to have a party.

    Ⓓ was the same as Mrs. Kern gave them.

5. What did the tape recorder play during the slide show?

    Ⓐ people asking for help

    Ⓑ songs about nature

    Ⓒ children's voices

    Ⓓ sounds from a rain forest

Founders of the Children's Rain Forest (continued)

Read the following questions carefully. Use complete sentences to answer the questions.

6. What made Mrs. Kern's students interested in the rain forest?

_____

_____

7. Why did Mrs. Kern expect Sharon Kinsman to laugh at her?

_____

_____

8. How did the students feel after Kinsman's slide show?

_____

_____

9. Why did the students keep raising money after their first big event?

_____

_____

10. What is the cause of Mrs. Kern's optimism at the end of the selection?

_____

_____

Founders of the Children's Rain Forest (continued)

Read the question below. Write complete sentences for your answer. Support your answer with information from the selection.

Linking to the Concepts Why is Mrs. Kern's rule about there being no bad ideas so important?

_____

_____

_____

_____

_____

Read the question below. Your answer should be based on your own experience. Write complete sentences for your answer.

Personal Response How can you be responsible every day for Earth and its environment?

_____

_____

_____

_____

_____

Founders of the Children's Rain Forest (continued)

Grammar, Usage, and Mechanics

Read each question. Fill in the bubble beside the answer in each group that is correct. If none of the answers is correct, choose the last answer, "none of the above."

1. In which sentence is a noun underlined?

Ⓐ The <u>icy</u> road made driving dangerous.

Ⓑ The icy road made driving <u>dangerous</u>.

Ⓒ The icy road <u>made</u> driving dangerous.

Ⓓ none of the above

2. In which sentence is a proper noun underlined?

Ⓐ The <u>airport</u> was crowded with European travelers.

Ⓑ The family took a winter vacation in <u>Florida</u>.

Ⓒ <u>Everyone</u> was excited to get to the Grand Canyon.

Ⓓ none of the above

3. In which sentence is an action verb underlined?

Ⓐ The fish <u>swam</u>.   Ⓒ The pond <u>seems</u> cold.

Ⓑ A tall bird <u>had</u> landed.   Ⓓ none of the above

4. In which sentence is a helping verb underlined?

Ⓐ The old bridge <u>looks</u> like it is all right.

Ⓑ A truck <u>damaged</u> the old bridge.

Ⓒ A new bridge <u>will</u> be built next year.

Ⓓ none of the above

5. In which sentence is the complete predicate underlined?

Ⓐ Our big dog sleeps on the couch <u>in the living room</u>.

Ⓑ <u>Our big dog</u> sleeps on the couch in the living room.

Ⓒ Our big dog <u>sleeps on the couch in the living room</u>.

Ⓓ none of the above

Founders of the Children's Rain Forest (continued)

Analyzing the Selection

Read the questions below. Write complete sentences for your response. Support your answer with information from the selection.

What do you think was the most surprising part of the selection? Why was it surprising to you?

_____

_____

_____

_____

_____

_____

_____

_____

_____

_____

_____

_____

Founders of the Children's Rain Forest (continued)

Oral Fluency Assessment

Going West

A fire crackled cheerfully in the kitchen fireplace as Nathan, Ishmael, Rachel, Mother, and Father sat down for dinner. Father seemed excited as he ladled stew into each bowl.

When everyone was served, he cleared his throat. "Your mother and I have some news. We are thinking about joining the wagon train going West."

Wide-eyed, Nathan and Isaac turned to one another and started whooping with excitement. Rachel, the youngest, was quiet. She was too young to understand what a trip like this meant.

"We could finally have some land of our own," said Mother.

Ishmael stood up. "When do we start packing?" he asked.

"Sit down, young man," Father chuckled. "If we go, we'll need to pack very thoughtfully, keeping in mind we can only bring the bare essentials. We'd need a rifle so we could hunt for food and an axe to cut wood and clear land. Mother would need to bring a couple of pots and pans to use for cooking and her spinning wheel to make fabric for clothing."

They could only bring what fit in their wagon, which would be pulled by a pair of oxen. "The lighter you travel, the easier it is," Father said. Jackson, the family dog, would probably go along. Jackson would assist with the hunting, and he could help protect the family during dangerous encounters.

Name _____ Date _____ Score _____

Jason and the Golden Fleece

Vocabulary

Read each item. Fill in the bubble for the answer you think is correct.

1. If something is **glistening,** it is

   Ⓐ dusty.   Ⓒ costly.

   Ⓑ dull.   Ⓓ shiny.

2. What is the meaning of the Greek root **naut?**

   Ⓐ sailor   Ⓒ night

   Ⓑ foot   Ⓓ plant

3. The monster had no **pity** for Jason. What is **pity?**

   Ⓐ money and gifts

   Ⓑ extra time and attention

   Ⓒ feelings of sorrow or sympathy

   Ⓓ advice or knowledge

4. The birds that swooped through the windows were **hideous. Hideous** means

   Ⓐ well-trained.

   Ⓑ very ugly.

   Ⓒ very ill.

   Ⓓ large.

5. The Clashing Cliffs were two rock walls on either side of a **strait.** In this sentence, a **strait** is

   Ⓐ a winding mountain path.

   Ⓑ a carved figurehead on a ship.

   Ⓒ a gate or entrance to a garden.

   Ⓓ a narrow passageway of water.

Jason and the Golden Fleece (continued)

Comprehension

Read the following questions carefully. Then completely fill in the bubble of each correct answer. You may look back at the selection to find the answer to each of the questions.

1. Why does King Pelias give Jason a challenge?

   (A) He wants to train Jason to be king.

   (B) He hopes to be rid of Jason.

   (C) He thinks Jason has become too proud.

   (D) He is tired of being king.

2. Why does Jason visit King Phineas?

   (A) He needs to know where to find the fleece.

   (B) He is told that the king owns the fleece.

   (C) He needs help gathering an army.

   (D) He hopes to borrow a ship from the king.

Jason and the Golden Fleece (continued)

3. How are the gulls different from the harpies?

Ⓐ They are birds.

Ⓑ They move in flocks.

Ⓒ They provide help.

Ⓓ They fly above the sea.

4. Which of these is a clue that the author provides to let the reader know the island king is up to no good?

Ⓐ The king lives in the land of Colchis.

Ⓑ The king curls his lip before he speaks.

Ⓒ The king tells Jason he can have the fleece.

Ⓓ The king has deep purple pockets.

5. Medea's potion puts Pelias to sleep

Ⓐ forever.

Ⓑ for three days.

Ⓒ for three months.

Ⓓ for three years.

Jason and the Golden Fleece (continued)

Read the following questions carefully. Use complete sentences to answer the questions.

6. Why does Jason bring the fleece home with him?

_____

_____

7. Why does Aeson at first refuse the crown of Thebes?

_____

_____

8. What causes Aeson to be king once again?

_____

_____

9. What happens to Pelias at the end of this myth?

_____

_____

10. What parts of this selection help classify it as a myth?

_____

_____

Jason and the Golden Fleece (continued)

Read the question below. Write complete sentences for your answer. Support your answer with information from the selection.

Linking to the Concepts In what ways does Jason show himself to be a hero?

_____

_____

_____

_____

_____

Read the question below. Your answer should be based on your own experience. Write complete sentences for your answer.

Personal Response How does it feel when someone helps you to succeed? Write about a time someone helped you succeed.

_____

_____

_____

_____

_____

Jason and the Golden Fleece (continued)

Grammar, Usage, and Mechanics

Read each item. Fill in the bubble for the answer you think is correct. If none of the answers is correct, choose the last answer, "none of the above."

1. Which sentence has a possessive noun?
   - Ⓐ Get ready or you will miss the bus.
   - Ⓑ The clock runs a little fast.
   - Ⓒ We will buy the farmer's corn.
   - Ⓓ none of the above

2. Which sentence has a correct plural form?
   - Ⓐ The two riveres join at this spot.
   - Ⓑ The children are climbing the branches of the tree.
   - Ⓒ Empty boxs were piled beside the door.
   - Ⓓ none of the above

3. Where could you find biographies of famous writers?
   - Ⓐ Online dictionary
   - Ⓑ Online encyclopedia
   - Ⓒ Web site for office supply store
   - Ⓓ none of the above

4. Which of these words is a pronoun?
   - Ⓐ catch
   - Ⓒ heavy
   - Ⓑ table
   - Ⓓ none of the above

5. Which sentence contains an object pronoun?
   - Ⓐ They went to practice a little while ago.
   - Ⓑ Call when you are ready to leave.
   - Ⓒ Mom waited for us after soccer practice.
   - Ⓓ none of the above

Jason and the Golden Fleece (continued)

Analyzing the Selection

Read the question below. Write complete sentences for your answer. Support your answer with information from the selection.

Why do you think Jason was willing to go through so much to get the Golden Fleece? Use information from the selection and your opinion to answer the question.

_____

_____

_____

_____

_____

_____

_____

_____

_____

_____

_____

_____

_____

Jason and the Golden Fleece (continued)

Oral Fluency Assessment

From the Country to the City

Alexander always enjoyed the outdoors. He had grown up on a farm so he was used to being outside all the time. He helped with all the chores around the farm and he spent his days cleaning out the barn, feeding the chickens and cutting wood for the fireplace. It did not seem like work; it was just what he did. When Alexander's family moved from the country to a big city, he really missed those days of being on the farm.

In the city, he did not have animals to care for. There were no wild animals that came to visit. In the country, all sorts of animals would stroll by the farm. He would see raccoons, rabbits, deer, and even a fox every now and then.

There was only one place nearby, on the outskirts of the city, where animals might show up. That was a park that was linked to open-space land the city owned. No houses or businesses could be built on the space, and some children said they had seen wild animals there. The open-space land looked like a small forest and stretched for miles. Alexander loved spending time there, and he and his friends enjoyed hiking there.

Name _____ Date _____ Score _____

The Quest for Healing

Vocabulary

Read each item. Fill in the bubble for the answer you think is correct.

1. Another word for **task** is

   Ⓐ path.

   Ⓑ wood.

   Ⓒ job.

   Ⓓ tool.

2. Which word fits in this base word family?
   _____, **kindly, kindness, kindliest**

   Ⓐ nice

   Ⓑ king

   Ⓒ unkind

   Ⓓ caring

3. On the third day, Nekumonta was **exhausted** and nearly gave up. **Exhausted** means

   Ⓐ frustrated.

   Ⓑ extremely tired.

   Ⓒ confident.

   Ⓓ out of food and ideas.

4. The animals of the forest showed **loyalty** to Nekumonta. **Loyalty** is

   Ⓐ bitterness and anger.

   Ⓑ mistrust and suspicion.

   Ⓒ surprise and wonder.

   Ⓓ support and affection.

5. After speaking with Nekumonta, the bear **lumbered** away. **Lumbered** means that the bear moved

   Ⓐ in a secret and sneaky way.

   Ⓑ with quiet and careful steps.

   Ⓒ in a slow and heavy way.

   Ⓓ with confidence and speed.

The Quest for Healing (continued)

Comprehension

Read the following questions carefully. Then completely fill in the bubble of each correct answer. You may look back at the selection to find the answer to each of the questions.

1. The saying "her days . . . were numbered" means that Shanewis

Ⓐ was still a young woman.

Ⓑ waited eagerly for spring.

Ⓒ was almost ready to die.

Ⓓ knew winter had arrived.

2. Why does Shanewis ask Nekumonta to take her outside?

Ⓐ The weather has turned beautiful.

Ⓑ The spirits of her ancestors are calling.

Ⓒ The villagers are having a gathering.

Ⓓ The disease is beginning to lift.

The Quest for Healing (continued)

3. Nekumonta leaves his wife in order to

Ⓐ avoid getting sick.

Ⓑ go and get her family.

Ⓒ collect some fire wood.

Ⓓ find some healing herbs.

4. Right after Nekumonta asks the bear for help, he

Ⓐ talks to a rabbit.

Ⓑ visits with a doe.

Ⓒ hears a sparkling chorus.

Ⓓ calls to the villagers.

5. The bear most likely leaves Nekumonta unharmed because he

Ⓐ knows that Nekumonta is good.

Ⓑ can tell that Nekumonta is becoming sick.

Ⓒ suspects that the great Manitou is watching.

Ⓓ knows that Shanewis is waiting for him.

The Quest for Healing (continued)

Read the following questions carefully. Use complete sentences to answer the questions.

6. Why does the Manitou decide to help the animals and Nekumonta?

_____

_____

7. How does the Manitou show Nekumonta where to look?

_____

_____

8. How does bathing in the Healing Waters change Nekumonta?

_____

_____

9. What do the villagers think of the Healing Waters?

_____

_____

10. What are two details that help to classify this as a make-believe story?

_____

_____

The Quest for Healing (continued)

Read the question below. Write complete sentences for your answer. Support your answer with information from the selection.

Linking to the Concepts How is the kindness Nekumonta shows to nature repaid?

_____

_____

_____

_____

_____

Read the question below. Your answer should be based on your own experience. Write complete sentences for your answer.

Personal Response What are some ways that you can show respect for plants and animals where you live?

_____

_____

_____

_____

_____

The Quest for Healing (continued)

Grammar, Usage, and Mechanics

Read each question. Fill in the bubble beside the answer in each group that is correct. If none of the answers is correct, choose the last answer, "none of the above."

1. In which sentence is a preposition underlined?

(A) The skiers <u>waited</u> for the chairlift to the top.

(B) The skiers waited <u>for</u> the chairlift to the top.

(C) The <u>skiers</u> waited for the chairlift to the top.

(D) none of the above

2. In which sentence is a prepositional phrase underlined?

(A) Shore birds walked <u>along the beach</u>.

(B) <u>Waves rolled</u> in one after another.

(C) At the far end of the beach were <u>some large sand dunes</u>.

(D) none of the above

3. What should you do to a document you need to work on later?

(A) delete it

(C) highlight it

(B) close it without saving

(D) none of the above

4. In which sentence is the adjective used correctly?

(A) This story is more funnier than the last one you told.

(B) This story is funnier than the last one you told.

(C) This story is more funner than the last one you told.

(D) none of the above

5. Which sentence is correct?

(A) The Most recenter game was the team's best.

(B) the more recenter game was the Teams Best.

(C) The most recent game was the team's best.

(D) none of the above

The Quest for Healing • **Lesson Assessment Book 2**

The Quest for Healing (continued)

Analyzing the Selections

Read the questions below. Write complete sentences for your answer. Support your answer with information from the selections.

Think about the three selections you have read in this unit. In each selection, people did remarkable things for a good reason. How were these people and their actions alike? How were they different?

_____

_____

_____

_____

_____

_____

_____

_____

_____

_____

_____

_____

The Quest for Healing (continued)

Oral Fluency Assessment

The Steel Drum

Drums have often been made out of everyday things, like trash can lids and empty barrels. One day, someone tried hammering out the end of a steel barrel. The sound he or she created was different. It was not quite right. Someone else tried shaping the barrel end the other way. It made a kind of bowl. Once people heard the beautiful sound this drum made, they knew that a new type of drum had been born.

Steel drums were invented on the island of Trinidad. The most expert steel drummers still live in that area. However, the steel drum is now played around the world. Steel drum music is often heard in parts of the United States, particularly in those areas where people from the Caribbean have come to live.

The sound of the steel drum is so wonderful that one drum is sometimes not enough. In many bands, several steel drums usually play together. Some large steel drum bands have as many as a hundred members. Each person plays a couple of drums.

There are many famous steel drum bands that perform and make recordings. These bands also compete in large annual contests. The bands practice together for many months. They hope to win a prize and a chance to become famous.

Name _____ **Date** _____ **Score** _____

The White Spider's Gift

Vocabulary

Read each item. Fill in the bubble for the answer you think is correct.

1. If something is **rare,** it is

Ⓐ tiny.

Ⓒ old.

Ⓑ beautiful.

Ⓓ unusual.

2. Which prefix means "before"?

Ⓐ *pre-*

Ⓒ *mid-*

Ⓑ *re-*

Ⓓ *dis-*

3. The chieftain says that Piki is good and **noble.** In this sentence, **noble** means that Piki

Ⓐ is a performer.

Ⓒ has an inner greatness.

Ⓑ fights like a warrior.

Ⓓ has great wealth.

4. The old woman says that the older you get, the more **burdened** with care you become. If you are **burdened,** you

Ⓐ are forgetful.

Ⓑ are weighed down with a heavy load.

Ⓒ enjoy remembering the past.

Ⓓ want to solve problems by yourself.

5. At the beginning of the selection, Spider is **pleading** with everyone she meets. **Pleading** means

Ⓐ saying kind things to others.

Ⓑ asking lots of different questions.

Ⓒ chatting cheerfully about things.

Ⓓ begging for something sincerely.

The White Spider's Gift (continued)

Comprehension

Read the following questions carefully. Then completely fill in the bubble of each correct answer. You may look back at the selection to find the answer to each of the questions.

1. In this selection, some words are inside parentheses ( ). The words inside the parentheses are meant to show

   Ⓐ what the director should do

   Ⓑ how the actors should act.

   Ⓒ what the actors should say.

   Ⓓ how the stage should look.

2. Who is the last person to refuse to help Spider in scene 1?

   Ⓐ a boy hunting for tea leaves

   Ⓑ a girl looking for flowers

   Ⓒ a woman gathering twigs

   Ⓓ a boy filling a jar with water

The White Spider's Gift • **Lesson Assessment Book 2**

The White Spider's Gift (continued)

3. Which of these is a hint about something that will happen later in the play?

   Ⓐ You are a good, strong young Guarani.

   Ⓑ A selfless heart is the strongest of all.

   Ⓒ Will you please place me back in my web so that I may rest?

   Ⓓ Someday I shall help you as you have helped me this day.

4. The Chieftain begins the competition by asking the boys

   Ⓐ to run a foot race.

   Ⓑ to shoot at a feather.

   Ⓒ to wrestle one another.

   Ⓓ to find the most beautiful gift.

5. Piki feels hopeless about winning because he

   Ⓐ loses all of the sports contests.

   Ⓑ is poor and cannot afford a nice gift.

   Ⓒ believes Kuma deserves to win.

   Ⓓ thinks the princess will hate his gift.

The White Spider's Gift (continued)

Read the following questions carefully. Use complete sentences to answer the questions.

6. In scene 1, what do Piki's actions suggest about him?

_____

_____

7. What is Spider's gift?

_____

_____

8. How can you tell that Spider works all night on the gift?

_____

_____

9. How is Kuma different from Piki?

_____

_____

10. Based on the tests that the Chieftain gives the boys, what kind of husband does he want for his daughter?

_____

_____

The White Spider's Gift (continued)

Read the question below. Write complete sentences for your answer. Support your answer with information from the selection.

Linking to the Concepts How does this selection support the saying, "One good deed deserves another"?

_____

_____

_____

_____

_____

Read the question below. Your answer should be based on your own experience. Write complete sentences for your answer.

Personal Response Do you think the Chieftain is a wise man? Explain your answer fully.

_____

_____

_____

_____

_____

The White Spider's Gift (continued)

Grammar, Usage, and Mechanics

Read each question. Fill in the bubble beside the answer in each group that is correct. If none of the answers is correct, choose the last answer, "none of the above."

1. In which sentence is the independent clause underlined?

Ⓐ The doctor told Nina <u>when she could play again</u>.

Ⓑ <u>The doctor told Nina</u> when she could play again.

Ⓒ The doctor told <u>Nina when she could</u> play again.

Ⓓ none of the above

2. In which sentence is the dependent clause underlined?

Ⓐ Dad stopped the car <u>when he heard a funny noise</u>.

Ⓑ <u>Dad stopped the car</u> when he heard a funny noise.

Ⓒ Dad <u>stopped the car when</u> he heard a funny noise.

Ⓓ none of the above

3. In which sentence do the subject and verb agree?

Ⓐ A range of mountains stand in the distance.

Ⓑ The explorers packs carefully for the trip.

Ⓒ Each of the explorers has a special talent.

Ⓓ none of the above

4. In which sentence do the subject and verb agree?

Ⓐ The bus routes is easy.   Ⓒ A group were waiting.

Ⓑ Each have a shelter.   Ⓓ none of the above

5. Which sentence has correct punctuation?

Ⓐ "We will open in an hour, said" the manager.

Ⓑ "We will open in an hour," said the manager.

Ⓒ "We will open in an hour, said the manager."

Ⓓ none of the above

The White Spider's Gift (continued)

Analyzing the Selection

Read the question below. Write complete sentences for your answer. Support your answer with information from the selection.

Many folktales have as their theme repaying a kindness or debt. Why do you think this theme is so important to people around the world? Use information from the selection, information you know already, and your opinion to answer the question.

_____

_____

_____

_____

_____

_____

_____

_____

_____

_____

_____

_____

The White Spider's Gift (continued)

Oral Fluency Assessment

The Anasazi Tribe

Can you imagine living under the side of a cliff in a huge apartment made out of stone and mud? An ancient tribe called the Anasazi used to live in such places. You can even visit these wonderful sites today. You can see how they lived.

The Anasazi lived in the Four Corners area of the Southwest. This area includes Utah, Colorado, New Mexico, and Arizona. The tribe lived a long time ago, from about A.D. 200 to A.D. 1300. We know when and where they lived from the ruins they left behind.

The Anasazi made their houses with walls of stone. This helped their homes stand up to storms and harsh winter snows. The homes were built under a cliff which gave them added protection. Some buildings were as high as four stories.

Within these structures were many rooms. Some had more than two hundred rooms. They housed some four hundred people. At the time of the Anasazi, tens of thousands of these dwellings existed. They dotted the land for miles and miles. Mesa Verde in the southwestern part of Colorado was the largest of these communities. The cliff dwellings there have given us the best picture of how this tribe lived.

Name _____ Date _____ Score _____

The Story of Annie Sullivan

Vocabulary

Read each item. Fill in the bubble for the answer you think is correct.

1. Which Latin root means "to see"?

Ⓐ *pod*　　　　　Ⓒ *void*

Ⓑ *spect*　　　　Ⓓ *terr*

2. Another word for **imitating** is

Ⓐ copying.　　　Ⓒ chatting.

Ⓑ teasing.　　　Ⓓ asking.

3. After not getting her way, Helen sat upstairs **sulking. Sulking** means that Helen was

Ⓐ playing with toys.

Ⓑ nibbling on the cake.

Ⓒ pouting and acting angry.

Ⓓ stomping and banging on things.

4. The Kellers were **disturbed** by the scene at the breakfast table. **Disturbed** means that they were

Ⓐ pleased.　　　Ⓒ unimpressed.

Ⓑ amused.　　　Ⓓ upset.

5. Annie **insistently** put the spoon in Helen's hand. If you do something **insistently,** you do it

Ⓐ while talking at the same time.

Ⓑ in a strong or firm manner.

Ⓒ with a puzzled look on your face.

Ⓓ in front of other people.

The Story of Annie Sullivan (continued)

Comprehension

Read the following questions carefully. Then completely fill in the bubble of each correct answer. You may look back at the selection to find the answer to each of the questions.

1. There is enough information in the selection to suggest that Sullivan

    (A) finds Helen to be a shy student.

    (B) was both a teacher and a trained nurse.

    (C) grew up near the Keller home.

    (D) had worked with blind people before.

2. When Sullivan arrives, it seems as if Helen's family has been

    (A) letting Helen do as she pleases.

    (B) looking for a new job for Helen.

    (C) trying to teach Helen to talk.

    (D) giving Helen too many sweets.

The Story of Annie Sullivan (continued)

3. According to Sullivan, what two things does Helen need to learn?

Ⓐ please and thank-you

Ⓑ obedience and love

Ⓒ letters and words

Ⓓ reading and arithmetic

4. Why does Sullivan ask if there is a place where she and Helen can be by themselves?

Ⓐ The Keller household is too noisy.

Ⓑ The Kellers live in a one-room house.

Ⓒ The Kellers keep getting involved.

Ⓓ The Keller children only want to play.

5. Helen realized that words actually stood for things when Sullivan

Ⓐ let her eat some cake.

Ⓑ taught her the difference between *mug* and *milk.*

Ⓒ spelled W-A-T-E-R in her hand.

Ⓓ showed her how to identify living creatures.

The Story of Annie Sullivan (continued)

Read the following questions carefully. Use complete sentences to answer the questions.

6. What kind of a teacher does Sullivan have to be in order to succeed with Helen?

_____

_____

7. When Sullivan first saw Helen, how did Helen look?

_____

_____

8. How does Sullivan change Helen's life?

_____

_____

9. When Helen gives Sullivan a hug "of her own accord," how does Sullivan feel?

_____

_____

10. Why is Helen so wild and rude at the beginning of the selection?

_____

_____

The Story of Annie Sullivan (continued)

Read the question below. Write complete sentences for your answer. Support your answer with information from the selection.

Linking to the Concepts How did the Keller family change because of Sullivan?

_____

_____

_____

_____

_____

_____

Read the question below. Your answer should be based on your own experience. Write complete sentences for your answer.

Personal Response What makes a great teacher? Use details from the selection and from your own experience to support your opinion.

_____

_____

_____

_____

_____

The Story of Annie Sullivan (continued)

Grammar, Usage, and Mechanics

Read each question. Fill in the bubble beside the answer in each group that is correct. If none of the answers is correct, choose the last answer, "none of the above."

1. In which sentence is the verb in the past tense?

   Ⓐ The mayor and town council meet once a month.

   Ⓑ The town bought an old farm just across the river.

   Ⓒ The old farm will become an agricultural museum.

   Ⓓ none of the above

2. In which sentence is the verb in the past perfect tense?

   Ⓐ The geese will start arriving soon.

   Ⓑ They spent the summer in Canada.

   Ⓒ Each fall, they fly thousands of miles.

   Ⓓ none of the above

3. In which sentence is the verb in the future tense?

   Ⓐ Robins build a nest.   Ⓒ The tree will have fruit.

   Ⓑ Blossoms appeared.   Ⓓ none of the above

4. Which sentence has correct punctuation?

   Ⓐ The cave was huge; it went miles into the mountain.

   Ⓑ The cave was; huge it went miles into the mountain.

   Ⓒ The cave was huge, it went miles, into the mountain.

   Ⓓ none of the above

5. Which sentence has correct punctuation?

   Ⓐ We went to three countries France Austria and Italy.

   Ⓑ We went to three countries: France, Austria, and Italy.

   Ⓒ We went to three countries, France: Austria: and Italy.

   Ⓓ none of the above

The Story of Annie Sullivan (continued)

Analyzing the Selection

Read the question below. Write complete sentences for your answer. Support your answer with information from the selections.

In the selections "Founders of the Children's Rain Forest" and "The Story of Annie Sullivan," teachers changed their students and the world forever. Why were the changes so important to the students and the world?

_____

_____

_____

_____

_____

_____

_____

_____

_____

_____

The Story of Annie Sullivan (continued)

Oral Fluency Assessment

Homes in America

Historic American homes come in many shapes and styles. In America's Southwest, many homes are built from adobe bricks. These are a combination of mud and straw. Adobe homes save energy. Heat from sunshine is stored in the walls in the winter. Those same walls keep the inside cool in summer. Since they look like earth, adobe houses blend in well with what is around them.

Wooden houses are found in many places. The first wooden houses were log cabins. Today's wooden buildings have what is called a "frame." Pieces of lumber are used to create a frame. Other materials are nailed on the frame to create the walls. Most houses made of wood are coated with one or more colors of paint. The paint is for protection and decoration. They must be repainted once in a while. This is something of a bother. However, it allows people to change the look of their house.

In some areas of North America, settlers built their homes out of stone. This stone was either slab stone from a quarry or river stone held together with mortar. Stone houses are the color of the local stone, which is usually grayish. These houses are rustic and natural looking.

Name _____ **Date** _____ **Score** _____

Persuasive Writing

Writing Situation
A cause that is important to you

Audience
Other students your age and their families

Directions for Writing
Think of something that is important to you. It can be something global, such as saving the rain forest, or something local, such as supporting an animal shelter. Explain what the cause is, and write about why it should be important to other people so they will support it as well.

Checklist
You will earn the best score if you
- think about your cause and why it is important to you.
- plan your writing before you begin.
- have a beginning paragraph that gets the attention of readers.
- state the cause clearly in the first paragraph.
- include facts or examples that show the cause to be important.
- state the cause several times in your writing.
- make clear what you expect the reader to do.
- show that you care about the cause.
- write in a way that is interesting to your readers.
- write complete sentences and avoid fragments or run-ons.